JOHNNY APPLESEED
STORYBOOK

Young Johnny Appleseed owned an orchard on a river bluff at the edge of a town called Pittsburgh. This was a long time ago, when Pittsburgh was the last town that pioneer families seeking new homes in the American wilderness would see.

Johnny worried as he watched people load their possessions on rafts and small boats to start down the Ohio River. Sometimes there were a hundred boats a day. He knew there were no apple trees in the mighty forests where these people would build new homes.

Without apples, there could be no juicy snacks for children to munch, no pies for dessert, and no way to make cider and vinegar.

Vinegar would be needed to make pickles and other good things which people needed in those days before they had refrigerators or freezers.

He started to give little bags of apple seeds to men and women, so they could plant them at their new homes. But Johnny knew it would be ten years before his seeds became trees big enough to have apples on them, and there would be hundreds of children growing up who would never have an apple to eat.

He decided he must go far into the wilderness, and plant trees that would be ready for families when they had their new log cabins built, and some land cleared for gardens.

So Johnny Appleseed sold his orchard, and gathered bag after bag of apple seeds that could make new trees. He started west, with his seeds and all he owned tied on the back of his horse.

He slept on the ground at night beside the narrow trail, and because he had walked all day leading his horse, he slept very soundly.

When he awoke one morning, he found that his horse was gone. He knew what had happened. The Indians, whose hunting grounds these had always been, did not like families who came from somewhere else, and cut down the trees to put up houses. They had taken Johnny's horse, to make him go back where he came from.

But Johnny Appleseed knew what he had to do. He threw away everything except his gun, the clothes he wore, and his bags of seeds and kept on walking west. He would have to plant one hundred seeds to be sure that one lived to become a tree good enough for him to transplant.

Two days' walk toward Marietta, Ohio, he found an Indian lying in the trail. He had been shot. Johnny bandaged the wound, and made a bed of brush for the man. Then he built a large fire, to guide tribe members who would look for their friend when he did not return to camp that night.

When the Indians found out what Johnny Appleseed had done for their friend, and why he was walking in the wilderness, they took him to their camp along a river and lent him a beautiful canoe made of birchbark. They told him he had only to float downstream and he would come to Marietta.

People in Marietta knew he was coming. Sailors in boats coming down the Ohio River from Pittsburgh had already told them about this man who would plant trees in the wilderness.

Johnny planted his first seeds before he left. He found just the right spot along a river, where he pulled up all the brush and weeds, then built a fence of poles and thorns around it. There he started planting his trees. He hired a man to keep his little garden clear of weeds and started down the Ohio River to a tiny settlement where the Indians had told him to leave the canoe.

People there had also heard he was coming, and they were so excited that they had already cleared land for his apple seeds.

Johnny Appleseed, leaving this time to plant seeds where no one had started towns yet, decided to leave his gun behind. He had already seen enough fighting and violence, and was sure that he could make friends with both the Indians and the settlers.

And he was right! The Indian whose life he had saved was Chief Logan, who sent word to other tribes to take care of this young man who walked alone. Settlers watched for him, and always had a meal and bed ready for Johnny.

And for years, Johnny Appleseed brought news to lonely settlements, and planted his seeds. He learned the language of the Indians, and he urged settlers to respect the tribes in whose land they were building.

Often barefoot, and wearing the saucepan in which he cooked upside down for a hat, he would show up unexpectedly at pioneer homes. There he would tell the latest news and read to them from a tattered Bible he kept dry by carrying it in his tin hat.

When the Indians sided with the British in the War of 1812, Johnny Appleseed, who spoke many native languages by then, became a hero. He ran through the trails faster than any war party, and saved hundreds of lives by warning settlers of coming attacks.

He spent the rest of his life moving always west just ahead of the families who were coming from the crowded cities of the east. Behind him he left trees full of greenings, spies, bellflowers and pippins; seed-no-further, never-fails, russets and rambos, for pioneer children who – until Johnny Appleseed returned to his orchards and carried a growing tree to their doorway – had never seen an apple.